What is doggy heaven?

By Darren Saligari

Illustrated by Austeja Slavickaite-Wojtczak

Rose-Grace Press

Yesterday my dog, Bella, died.

I cried and cried and cried.

Mum said it was an accident and nobody's to blame.

Not Bella, me or the bus driver, Mr James.

Now Bella's passed away and gone to doggy heaven.
It's where all dogs go when they die my mum reckons.
Doggy heaven? I'd never heard of that place before.
Is it like the park, the beach or is it some kind of store?

'Well,' said Mum, 'it's some of those things but it's so much more.
It's for dogs of all shapes and sizes who aren't alive anymore.
Doggy heaven is the most wonderful place.
It's full of bones, flying frisbees and other dogs to chase.'

'But where is it?' I asked 'and how do I get there?
Can I get there by car or train or flying chair?'

'It's not a place we can go,' said Mum. 'It's beyond the clouds, way up high.
Far beyond the big blue sky, higher than the highest high.'
'But,' I stammered, 'how did Bella get way up in the sky?
She's a dog and everyone knows that dogs can't fly!'

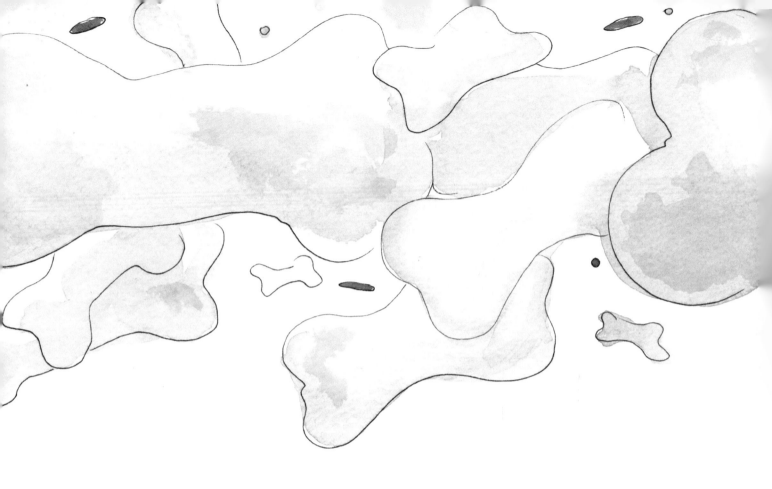

'She didn't fly or climb or jump,
nor did she take an elevator.
When doggies die they find their way,
on the rainbow escalator.'

'All right,' I said, 'I guess this doggy heaven place sounds OK.
But if I can't go there maybe Bella can come back some day?'
'Sadly not my dear, once you're there you can't come back.
Doggy heaven is a one-way ticket, there's no way to backtrack.'

'But who will pat Bella, kiss her goodnight and feed her treats?
Give her hugs and lots of love, and ride with her in the back seat?'

'In doggy heaven, Bella will have everything she needs and more.
And plenty of space where she can roam free and explore.
Bella may no longer be here with us it's true,
just know that she is safe and happy and thinking of you.'

'And when you look out of your window each night,
Bella will be the star that is shining extra bright.'

'I know it hurts to lose a doggy friend,
but I promise that this pain will pass, it will come to an end.
Now it's time to rest your head and close your eyes.
Have happy dreams about Bella and whisper your goodbyes.'

For Maddy & Ava

In memory of Bella

First published in 2018 by Rose-Grace Press

Australia

A catalogue record for this book is available from the National Library of Australia

ISBN: 978-0-9925024-1-6

whatisdoggyheaven.com

Made in United States
North Haven, CT
08 August 2023

40104868R00015